ALL ABOUT CAMP ROCK

PaRragon

Bath New York Singapore Hong Kong Cologne Delhi Melbourne

First published by Parragon in 2008

Parragon
Queen Street House
4 Queen Street
Bath BA1 1HE, UK

Based on "Camp Rock," Written by Karin Gist & Regina Hicks and Julie Brown & Paul Brown

ISBN 978-1-4075-3896-9

Printed in China

WHAT'S INSIDE...

CAMP ROCK PHOTO STORY

Follow the story of the summer that Mitchie will never forget with these awesome photos!

Mitchie dreams of making the most of her songwriting talent – she'd do anything to make her dreams of super-stardom come true!

A summer at the famous Camp Rock is all that Mitchie wants. There are only so many times you can practise being a rock star before you need to go out there and make it happen!

Mitchie's mum becomes the chef at Camp Rock, and Mitchie gets to attend the camp's classes. The only problem: Micthie has to help her mum out in the kitchen all summer long!

Shane Gray is a member of the band Connect Three, and a former Camp Rock-er. But fame and fortune have gone to Shane's head and his record company force him back to the camp to remind him where he came from!

Mitchie is totally star-struck when she meets Tess, the daughter of an award-winning singer. Mitchie is so desperate to impress Tess that she lies about who she is.

Shane does not want to be at Camp Rock! His uncle tries to cheer him up but Shane would rather be anywhere else.

Mitchie thinks no one is listening as she sings – little does she know that her voice has captivated Shane Gray!

Mitchie is shy about her songwriting talents, and is nervous to show her new friends what she's capable of.

Brown convinces Mitchie to have more confidence in her talents.

Shane leads the campers in a hip-hop dance class!

Mitchie, Peggy and Ella sing back up for Tess. But talented singers can't stay in the background forever...

Shane and the Connect Three boys blow the campers away at Beach Jam!

Caitlyn, Tess and Mitchie get involved in a messy food fight in the camp's cafeteria.

Caitlyn is sent to work in the camp's kitchen as a punishment for throwing food. It won't be long before Mitchie's secret is discovered...

Shane just can't stop thinking about the mysterious voice he heard at the beginning of the summer – he has to find the person behind that voice!

When Tess discovers that Mitchie is the girl that Shane's looking for, she does everything she can to stop Mitchie from singing at Final Jam – including framing her for stealing!

Mitchie's secret is out! Everyone at the camp knows that her mother is a cook and not a music executive, but no one is more upset that Shane – he trusted Mitchie.

The end of the summer is here! The campers take part in Final Jam to battle it out for a chance to record with world-famous rockers Connect Three.

Shane finally hears Mitchie sing and realizes that hers is the voice he's been thinking about all summer.

The campers celebrate the end of the summer and look forward to next year at Camp Rock!

CONNECT THREE
SPOT THE DIFFERENCE

Connect Three are the coolest Camp Rock graduates – they're world-famous superstars! Look at their pictures closely; can you spot the five differences between them?

CONNECT THREE'S MEMORY GAME

Look at this picture for 15 seconds. Cover it up and try to answer the questions below – good luck!

What colour is Nate's guitar?

What does it say on the side of the stage?

How many sails can you see in the background? 7

What is Shane wearing on his face? Glasses

What colour is the banner at the back of the stage?

WHAT'S YOUR MUSICAL STYLE?

Always wanted to know what your musical style is and where your talents should be directed? Take this quiz to find out!

1. **If you were going to appear on a TV talent show, what song would you sing?**

   A. A rock anthem.
   B. A pop song.
   C. A gentle ballad accompanied by acoustic guitar.

2. **Think about your favourite song. What does it sound like?**

   A. Loud and shouty, with lots of banging drums!
   B. Bouncy and fun, with a catchy chorus.
   C. Slow and mournful, with words which bring tears to your eyes.

3. **You're hanging out in your bedroom, feeling a bit bored. What do you do?**

   A. Plug in your electric guitar, turn up the amps, and away you go!
   B. Choreograph a new dance routine.
   C. Write some poetry.

4. **What's your wardrobe style?**

   A. Jeans and t-shirts. Mostly in different shades of black.
   B. Girlie and fun, mini-skirts and pink sassy tops.
   C. Floaty and baggy, lots of long skirts and layering.

5. **How do you dance to your favourite song?**

   A. Hair down and head banging, jumping up and down!
   B. Bopping around in a perfectly synchronised routine.
   C. You can't really call it dancing. It's more like swaying.

6. What kind of make-up do you wear?

A. Dark eyeliner with lots of black mascara
B. Pretty pink gloss, with subtle eye make-up.
C. You don't wear make-up.

MOSTLY As: You're a Rock Chick! You love music that you can just rock out to! You like to turn the volume up loud, and just get lost in the drums and guitars. If you can jump around to it, and your parents don't like it – you think it's perfect!

MOSTLY Bs: You're a Pop Princess! You love pop music, with catchy, fun lyrics and a bouncy tune. You quite often watch music videos so you can learn the proper choreographed routines and are never happier than when you're bopping along to a cool chart-topper.

MOSTLY Cs: You're A Soul Sensation! You love the emotions that a good song can evoke. You've probably cried along to a sad song more than once. But you also love to write your own lyrics and poetry, and are often seen scribbling down meaningful words in your notebook.

FIND A MATCHING MITCHIE PAIR

Mitchie has the biggest smile anywhere in Camp Rock! Check out these pictures of everyone's favourite camper – can you find a matching pair?

SHANE GRAY GUIDE TO ROCKSTARDOM!

Do you dream of Rockstardom? Well make your dreams come true by following Shane's top rock star tips?

You have to be a certain kind of person to make it as a superstar, and the first rule is that you need heaps of energy. Even before you're touring and performing shows six nights a week, you need unlimited energy to rehearse, audition and to keep putting yourself forward and pushing people to give you that all important first break. Sometimes this is the hardest part of becoming a superstar – even more exhausting than the demands to tour and record once you've **HIT THE TOP!**

Keep your energy levels high by eating loads of fresh fruit and vegetables, drinking at least six glasses of water a day and getting your body moving. Whether it's dancing around your bedroom, playing netball with your friends or going for a long walk in the countryside, when your blood is pumping you will feel revitalized and motivated.

Finally, its a good idea to do some research and get inspired by reading about your favourite superstars and how they made it to the top – some of them used to be just like you, which proves **YOU CAN MAKE IT TO THE TOP TOO!**

BE YOURSELF!

Stay true to yourself and the things that are important to you. Don't get caught up in the craziness of the music industry – you don't want to end up like Connect Three and be pushing records that your heart's not really into. The most important thing is to believe in yourself. If you don't believe you can make it, then you can't expect anyone else to!

You need a thick skin if you're going to be a superstar, because even at the best of times you'll have to deal with criticism and rejection. It's easy to let this put you off, but show your star quality from the start by keeping an up-beat attitude and staying positive about things and you'll be well on your way to becoming a teen idol! Try to take criticism constructively and use it to make your performance better. And remember, nobody gets the first thing they audition for. Look on your early auditions as practice for the big one when it comes along, and then if you are successful straight away, it's a bonus!

As a member of Connect Three, I'm lucky enough to have been very successful, but I make bad decisions sometimes, too – like putting out records that I didn't really like just because my record company told me to! When that happens, it's best to just accept that it was a mistake and move on.

FICKLE FAME

Once you've hit the big time, all the extra attention you receive can come as a bit of a shock. You may find that people who never even spoke to you before suddenly want to be your friends and that people you considered good friends before might start acting differently towards you. It can be a bit confusing! It might be worth reminding your friends that you're still the same person you always were, and you still want to be their friend and do the same fun things that you always did together. **REMEMBER THAT FRIENDSHIP USUALLY LASTS LONGER THAN FAME!**

It's not only people you knew before becoming a superstar who'll be changing their attitude towards you – you'll have fans that you've never even met before chasing you down the street **DEMANDING YOUR AUTOGRAPH OR A PICTURE!** I'll never forget the first time that happened to me – I was totally thrilled and absolutely petrified at the same time! Remember it's your fans who put you where you are, though, and they're the ones keeping you there, so even when you really don't feel like signing another CD, or posing with a complete stranger, just keep smiling and be polite, because – to your fans – meeting you is a once-in-a-lifetime experience. Try to enjoy it as much as they do!

PRESS PRESSURE

As a superstar, you'll need to know how to deal with the press. A big part of being a pop star is promoting your latest CD by doing photo shoots and interviews for magazines. Make sure you have a good idea about the image you want to project before you begin and try to steer the photographer or journalist in that direction. It's amazing how you can turn a question around from something that you don't want to talk about to something that you do – **LIKE HOW YOUR FANS ARE GOING TO LOVE YOUR LATEST CD!**

AHEAD OF THE GAME

It feels fantastic when you first make it to the dizzying heights of super-stardom, but remember that the hard work is only just beginning! It's easy to get over-excited about the fame and fortune and spend all your time shopping and hanging out with your new celebrity friends. That can be great fun for you, but it won't keep your fans happy, and before long they'll forget all about you and move on to the next up-and-coming superstar who is still working hard to rehearse, perform and record new CDs.

Keep your look fresh and always try to be ahead of the game. A great way to stay on top of things is to look at what is going on around you – not only in the pop world, but in fashion, movies and even among your friends at school. Visit an art gallery or read about life in a far away country – you can use anything to inspire you! Most importantly of all, keep rehearsing. If singing and dancing are what shot you to fame, then you need to practise and improve those skills all the time to keep you where you are.

FRIENDS FIRST

When you're on the road all the time, or rushing from recording studio to photo shoot and on to meet your agent, it can get very lonely. Sometimes I might speak to twenty people in one day, but not feel like I've actually connected with anyone! It sounds crazy, but it's possible to feel completely alone even when you're surrounded with people. That's why it's important to make time for yourself and for your friends. No one knows you better than your best friends, right? So take five minutes to call them up for a chat, or – even better – take a night off so you can just hang out together, because it doesn't matter how famous you are, you always need friends.

So, those are my **TOP TIPS FOR RISING STARS** – I hope you find them helpful! Finally, you always need a little bit of luck on the road to success, so good luck achieving your dreams – whatever they may be!

CAMPFIRE GAMES

Get your friends together, gather around the campfire and fill your evening with fun! Check out some of the awesome game ideas below!

Double As A Superstar!

Try this twist on charades! Each player takes a turn acting out a crazy Camp Rock moment. You and your friends get to be Mitchie, Shane, Tess, whoever you want! It can be anything – a dance, a song, a conversation. There's a catch (of course)! You can't actually speak or sing, you have to act it out. But, don't make the game TOO hard (otherwise it won't be fun). Before you take your turn, tell your players if they should be guessing a song, a person or moment.

Bluffing

Each person says three things, two of which are true and one is a lie! Take it in turns to seek out the truth.

Would You Rather...

This is a fun game to get to know things about your best friends that you would never have guessed! Ask the questions and start the laughs!

WOULD YOU RATHER:
Be a pop star or a runway model?

WOULD YOU RATHER:
Be Tess or Mitchie?

WOULD YOU RATHER:
Be super-famous or super-smart?

WOULD YOU RATHER:
Have five sisters or five brothers?

WOULD YOU RATHER:
Go swimming or ice skating?

WOULD YOU RATHER:
Be Mitchie or Caitlyn?

WOULD YOU RATHER:
Be invisible or be able to fly?

WOULD YOU RATHER:
Have a really bad haircut or be wearing a really hideous outfit?

WOULD YOU RATHER:
Crush on Shane or Nate?

WOULD YOU RATHER:
Be grounded for a month or not allowed to shop for six months?

WOULD YOU RATHER:
Have lots of friends who don't know you that well or one really good friend who knows you inside and out?

Which character are you (post-it note on head)

Give every guest a post-it note and ask them to write the name of a Camp Rock character on it and not to show anyone else. Then get everyone to stick their name onto the forehead of the person on their left. Take it in turns to ask everyone questions about the name on your forehead!

ODD TESS OUT

Tess loves to pose! Can you spot which posing picture is different from the others?

THROW A CAMP ROCK PARTY!

Celebrate your love for all things Camp Rock by throwing a Camp Rock party! Use these next few pages to plan your party in the finest detail.

Date and time

Day time   Evening   Late night

Venue

Camper's Cabin   Beach   Club House

Music to be played

Rock   Pop   Soul

Food

Chips 'n' Dips   Sushi   BBQ

Drinks

Fizzy   Fruit Punch   Water

Games we can play

⭐ Pin the tail ⭐   Musical chairs ⭐   ⭐ Would you rather ⭐

Dream musical guests

Shane Gray   Mitchie Torres   Tess Tyler

My present wishes

Guitar   Keyboard   Karaoke machine

Gift Voucher

What I'm going to wear

⭐ Fancy dress ⭐   ⭐ Fresh 'n' funky ⭐   ⭐ Cool 'n' casual ⭐

CAMP ROCKIN' STAR STYLE!

Are you a fashion-conscious rocker? Do you like to look sizzlin' as well as sounding slammin'? Well the next few pages are packed with top tips on how to dress like a superstar!

If you're laid-back and prefer comfort over style then check out Mitchie's tips for dressing like a future rock star.

If image is everything to you'd then you better check out Tess's tips on how to look like the ultimate red carpet diva!

Take a peek inside the wardrobe of tomorrow's biggest superstar!

HI GUYS!

MY STYLE IS KINDA CASUAL. I LOVE TO LOOK GOOD BUT I'M MORE INTERESTED IN MAKING MUSIC THAN WORRYING ABOUT FASHION! I LOVE TO WEAR JEANS AND BRIGHT TOPS – LOUD COLOURS ARE FUN COS THEY MAKE ME FEEL SO CONFIDENT!

Check out my awesome mustard-coloured boots! Not only are these boots really comfortable and practical – they make me stand out in a crowd! Never be scared to accessorize confidently and colourfully!

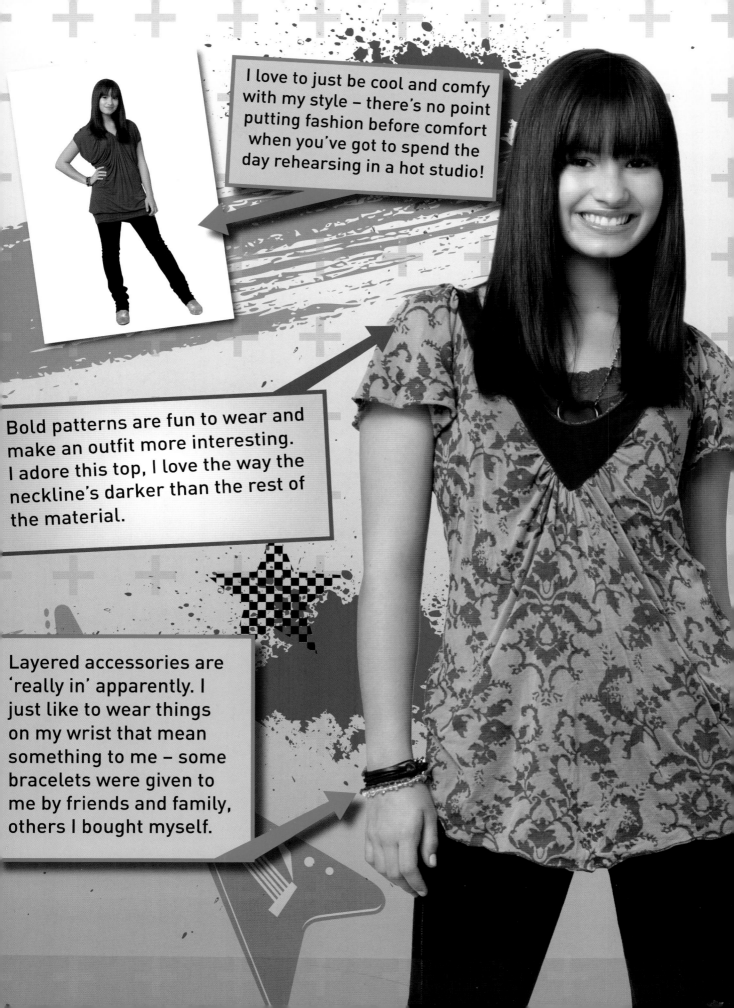

I love to just be cool and comfy with my style – there's no point putting fashion before comfort when you've got to spend the day rehearsing in a hot studio!

Bold patterns are fun to wear and make an outfit more interesting. I adore this top, I love the way the neckline's darker than the rest of the material.

Layered accessories are 'really in' apparently. I just like to wear things on my wrist that mean something to me – some bracelets were given to me by friends and family, others I bought myself.

STAR STYLE: TESS

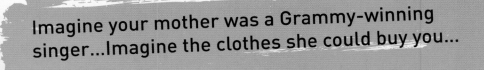

Imagine your mother was a Grammy-winning singer...Imagine the clothes she could buy you...

HEY!

SO, I CAN PRETTY MUCH PICK AND CHOOSE MY LOOK ON A DAY-TO-DAY BASIS. WHENEVER MY MOTHER GOES ON TOUR SHE SENDS ME CLOTHES FROM ALL AROUND THE WORLD. NOTHING IS TOO EXPENSIVE FOR ME – WHATEVER I WANT, I USUALLY GET.

If you want people to think you're a superstar then you gotta start dressing like one! I like my clothes to be sleek and stylish. Straight white jeans, wedge shoes and a bright top scream 'pop star of tomorrow'!

You got to have attitude if you're gonna make it in this business and I've got tons of it! I love to dress to impress, why settle for second best when you can be perfect?

Cashmere, silk, satin and Egyptian cotton are all fabrics that feel great against skin – a lot of my clothes are made from very expensive materials.

Solid colours make a confident statement – I'm a girl who knows what I want and knows how to get it!

Check out the detail on my jeans, I love to customize my clothes – it's always good to be as individual as possible if you want to stand out in a crowd.

STAR SECRETS:
MITCHIE TORRES

GREATEST DREAM:
To attend the prestigious Camp Rock and learn what it takes to become a singing sensation.

CAN BE FOUND:
Writing songs, singing in her bedroom, pounding raw meat into burgers (she helps out with her mum's catering business!) and slamming some awesome moves in hip-hop class!

FUNNIEST MOMENT:
Covering her face with flour in an attempt to hide her identity from Shane!

BEST QUOTE:
"You'll never know unless you try".

mitchie

Spending her summer at the famous Camp Rock is a dream come true for Mitchie Torres. So when Connie, Mitchie's Mum, announces that she's got a job catering at Camp Rock and Mitchie can attend the camp's classes, the budding superstar is beside herself with excitement!

But Mitchie soon discovers that the competition in the Camp Rock classroom is tough. Plus, amongst the crowds of cool music students Mitchie feels ashamed of who she is. The talented singer starts to lie about her family and is soon caught up in a web of her own deception. Before she knows it, Mitchie's dream summer soon turns into a nightmare.

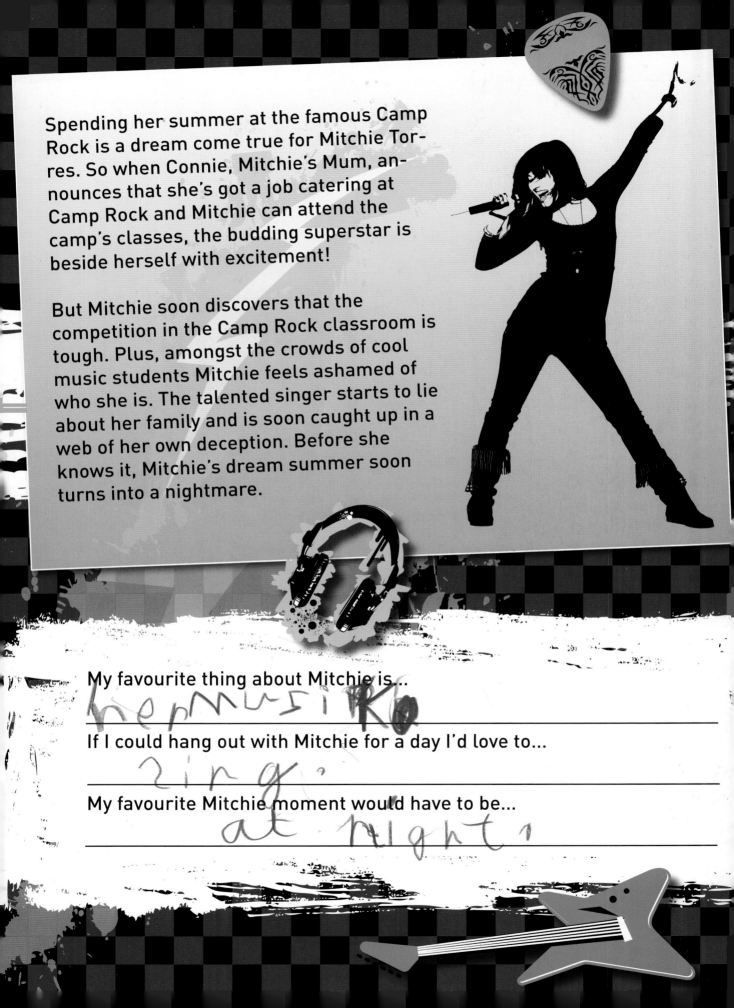

My favourite thing about Mitchie is...

her musik o

If I could hang out with Mitchie for a day I'd love to...

2ing.

My favourite Mitchie moment would have to be...

at night.

STAR SECRETS:
SHANE GRAY

GREATEST DREAM:
To find his own sound and play the music that he really loves with his band, Connect Three.

CAN BE FOUND:
Sitting by the water's edge playing his guitar and writing songs, looking for the girl with 'that voice', teaching hip-hop dance classes.

FUNNIEST MOMENT:
Shane is pretty cool and doesn't like to play the clown, but he always has fun hanging out with the other Connect Three guys.

BEST QUOTE:
"You're the voice I hear inside my head, the reason that I'm singing".

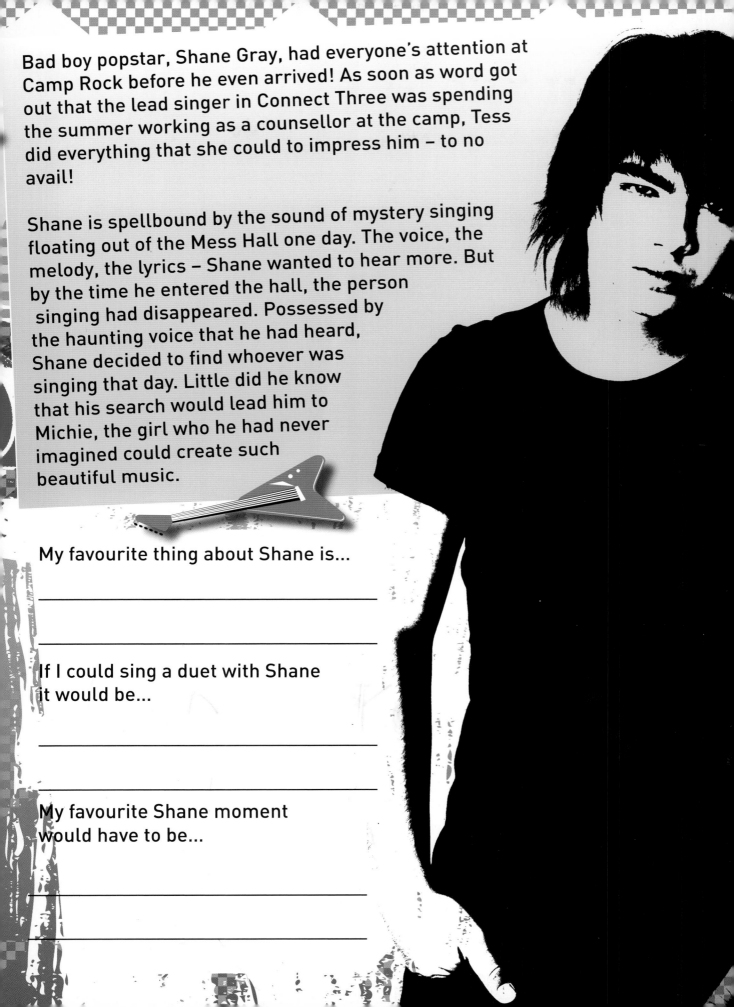

Bad boy popstar, Shane Gray, had everyone's attention at Camp Rock before he even arrived! As soon as word got out that the lead singer in Connect Three was spending the summer working as a counsellor at the camp, Tess did everything that she could to impress him – to no avail!

Shane is spellbound by the sound of mystery singing floating out of the Mess Hall one day. The voice, the melody, the lyrics – Shane wanted to hear more. But by the time he entered the hall, the person singing had disappeared. Possessed by the haunting voice that he had heard, Shane decided to find whoever was singing that day. Little did he know that his search would lead him to Michie, the girl who he had never imagined could create such beautiful music.

My favourite thing about Shane is...

_____

_____

If I could sing a duet with Shane it would be...

_____

_____

My favourite Shane moment would have to be...

_____

_____

STAR SECRETS:
TESS TYLER

GREATEST DREAM:
To be as famous and successful as her mother, T. J. Tyler.

CAN BE FOUND:
Bossing around her backup singers, conspiring ways to get rid of her competition and trying, and failing, to speak to her mother over the phone.

FUNNIEST MOMENT:
Any time she's put in her place! Underneath it all Tess isn't that special, and it's always funny to watch her being reminded of that.

BEST QUOTE:
"I'm too cool for this dress."

Tess is the daughter of the award winning singer T. J. Tyler. Tess loves to boast about who her mum is and make others feel inferior to her because of it. The other campers at Camp Rock all look up to Tess, especially her loyal followers Peggy and Ella.

But underneath her designer clothes, her nasty attitude and her bossiness, Tess isn't as confident as she makes out. Firstly, she hates anyone with any talent – she sees them as a threat. So when new camper Mitchie starts hanging around Tess she soon realized to keep quiet about her song writing ability. Plus, despite T. J. Tyler being so rich she can buy her daughter anything to make her happy, all Tess really wants is for her mum to be around more.

The best thing about Tess is...

If Tess asked me to be her backup singer I'd say...

My favourite Tess moment would have to be...

ULTIMATE CAMP ROCK QUIZ

TAKE THIS AWESOME QUIZ TO SEE JUST HOW BIG A FAN OF CAMP ROCK YOU ARE! ANSWERS AT THE END OF THE BOOK.

1. What is the name of Shane Gray's band?

2. Name Tess's famous mother.

3. Whose hair is this? *Nics*

4. What does Caitlyn want to be when she grows up?

a gitar ge

5. Finish the song lyrics: 'You're the voice I hear inside my head...'

6. Whose real name is Margaret Dupree?

7. Who do these shoes belong to?

MItchiE

8. What does Jason ask Shane to make for him?

9. Why does Mitchie get up early every morning whilst she's
at Camp Rock?

10. What does Shane's manager send to the Camp Rock kitchens?

11. Who is playing the guitar?

12. What is Tess's cabin known as?

13. What does Micthie tell Tess her mother does for a living?

14. What is the prize for winning Final Jam?

15. What instrument is Mitchie playing when Shane hears her sing for the first time?

16. Shane gets upset when he hears his music being referred to as 'cookie cutter...'

17. Whose belt is this?

18. What does Tess accuse Mitchie and Caitlyn of stealing?

19. How is Brown related to Shane?

20. What does Tess say to Mitchie at the end of Final Jam?

ANSWERS

Pg 42. Ulimate Camp Rock Quiz Answers

1. Connect Three
2. T. J. Tyler
3.

4. A music producer
5. '...The reason that I'm singing'.
6. Peggy
7.

8. A bird house
9. To help her mother in the kitchens.
10. A list of Shane's allergies.
11.

12. The Vibe Cabin
13. Run Hot Tunes TV, China.
14. Recording a duet with Shane Gray.
15. A piano
16. Pop star garbage
17.

18. Tess's charm bracelet
19. Shane's his uncle
20. 'See you next year.'